Barry Manilow's

COPACABANA

VOCAL SELECTIONS

BMG
MUSIC PUBLISHING

Exclusive Distributors:

Music Sales Limited
8/9 Frith Street, London W1V 5TZ, England.

Music Sales Pty Limited
120 Rothschild Avenue, Rosebery, NSW 2018, Australia.

This book © Copyright 1994 by BMG Music Publishing.
Order No. AM92678
ISBN 0-7119-4792-9

Music arranged by Roger Day.
Music processed by Paul Ewers Music Design.
Photographs courtesy of Clive Barda.

Your Guarantee of Quality:
As publishers, we strive to produce every book to the highest commercial standards.

The music has been freshly engraved and, whilst endeavouring to retain
the original running order of the soundtrack album, this book has been carefully designed
to minimise awkward page turns and to make playing from it a real pleasure.

Particular care has been given to specifying acid-free, neutral-sized
paper made from pulps which have not been elemental chlorine bleached.
This pulp is from farmed sustainable forests and was produced with special regard for the environment.
Throughout, the printing and binding have been planned to ensure a sturdy,
attractive publication which should give years of enjoyment. If your copy fails to meet
our high standards, please inform us and we will gladly replace it.

Music Sales' complete catalogue describes thousands of titles and is
available in full colour sections by subject, direct from Music Sales Limited.
Please state your areas of interest and send a cheque / postal order for £1.50 for postage to:
Music Sales Limited, Newmarket Road, Bury St. Edmunds, Suffolk IP33 3YB.

Printed in the United Kingdom by
J.B. Offset Printers (Marks Tey) Limited, Marks Tey, Essex.

COPACABANA
(Opening Sequence)

Music by Barry Manilow. Lyrics by Bruce Sussman & Jack Feldman.

at the Co - pa Co - pa - ca - ba - na.___

JUST ARRIVED

Music by Barry Manilow. Lyrics by Bruce Sussman & Jack Feldman.

and though my knees are shak-ing,___ I'm mak-ing___ my

stand. It all starts now, I can

see my name in ne-on. I won't al-

low a-ny cloud to rain on me.

19

ALL

fun of___ is one of___ a kind. It all starts

now, look who's cur - rent - ly ap - pear - ing.

This girl's a wow, all the ma - ga - zines a -

gree. I'll take my bow and the world will all be

21

cheer - ing just for me. New York or bust, I've just ar -

rived.____

Hey!____ Some - bo - dy said they're au -

Which way's Up - town?

gree. I'll take my bow and the

a - ny cloud would dare to rain on me, oh wow.

world will all be cheer - ing just for me.

That's me, I'll be on some mar - quee, ga - ther - ing dust, I

just sur - vived. Now New York or bust, I've

Now New York or bust, I've

25

just ar - - - rived._____

just ar - - - rived._____

LOLA
Hey world, I've just ar -

rived!_____

DANCIN' FOOL

Music by Barry Manilow. Lyrics by Bruce Sussman & Jack Feldman.

Vamp and repeat ad lib.

Vamp and repeat ad lib.

30

TONY & BOYS

When those trum-pets blare man,—

I ain't got a care man,— I'm like Fred A-staire— man,— cool!

31

Just give me a chance___ and___

my Tux - e - do pants___ and___

pre-sto!

TONY

I'm a dan - cin' fool.

ALL

I'm a danc-in' fool, yeah!

MAN WANTED

Music by Barry Manilow. Lyrics by Bruce Sussman & Jack Feldman.

33

NIGHT ON THE TOWN

Music by Barry Manilow. Lyrics by Bruce Sussman & Jack Feldman.

40

LOLA

Music by Barry Manilow. Lyrics by Bruce Sussman & Jack Feldman.

Lo - la would she stop me if I stole a

kiss, like this? Lo - la, if on - ly your

name were Sue 'cause Sue rhymes with skies of

blue, and morn - ing dew, and I love

Segue: "Who Needs To Dream?"

43

WHO NEEDS TO DREAM?

Music by Barry Manilow & Artie Butler. Lyrics by Bruce Sussman & Jack Feldman.

true.

Who needs to dream when there is you?

Who needs a hea-ven? For my whole life through who needs to

dream? You're my dream come true, ev-'ry dream, all come

Largo

true, my dream come true.

AY CARAMBA!

Music by Barry Manilow. Lyrics by Bruce Sussman & Jack Feldman.

- ram - ba!)

49

sist.

Can't stop the

con - gas,— tim - ba - les,— the bon - gos,— the cla - ves— and

1. **2.**

ay ay ay. Ay Ca - ay, ay Ca -

ram - ba.—

14 bar percussion break

Can't stop the con-gas— tim-ba-les,— the bon-gos,— the cla-ves,— the rum-ba,— the sam-ba,— the mam-bo,— la bam-ba— and ay ay ay, ay Ca-ram-ba._____

Verse 2:
I hear the rumba
(You hear the rumba?)
And then the mambo
(You want to mambo?)
Wait, I think you should know
Latin drums make me go
¡Ay Caramba!
They shake maracas
(I shake maracas)
I go bananas
(You like bananas?)
We start having fun
But before it's all done
¡Ay Caramba!

Oh those crazy, caressing
Caribbean rhythms,
To some it's "so what?"
To me it's so hot.

Can't stop the rumba,
The samba, the mambo,
La bamba and ¡Ay ay ay!
¡Ay Caramba!

BOLERO DE AMOR

Music by Barry Manilow. Lyrics by Bruce Sussman & Jack Feldman.

RICO

2° There are times we live as if in a dream, Drawn by a heart to a dis- tant

door, one that op - ens for a mo - ment to a world_____ that you've nev - er known be -

fore. Were you real or were you part of a dream, call - ing to me from a- cross the

SWEET HEAVEN

Music by Barry Manilow. Lyrics by Bruce Sussman & Jack Feldman.

64

WHO AM I KIDDING?

Music by Barry Manilow. Lyrics by Bruce Sussman & Jack Feldman.

GLADYS

Cas-

A♭/C

tel - li, Cas-tel-li, ya got-ta stop Cas-tel-li, the kid don't know him like we

D7(♭5)   G7   Cm

do.   Be-fore he's fin-ished wit'-cha well you'll ne-ver know what hit'-cha and it

D7   Gm   N.C.   Fm
                                            SAM

ain't a pret-ty pit'-cha, I tell you.   Al-right, al-right I'm go-ing, I'm go-ing, that

70

71

SAM (And I got haemorrhoids)

you, a sweet old fart like you.

74

WHO AM I KIDDING
(Reprise)

Music by Barry Manilow. Lyrics by Bruce Sussman & Jack Feldman.

THIS CAN'T BE REAL

Music by Barry Manilow. Lyrics by Bruce Sussman & Jack Feldman.

steal. The truth is-n't what it

seems, the truth is our wild-est dreams.

rall.

molto rall. STEPHEN

She's

a tempo

mere-ly a dream, I know, so why do I want her

WELCOME TO HAVANA

Music by Barry Manilow. Lyrics by Bruce Sussman & Jack Feldman.

Spoken: Señoras y Señores aqui esta la estrella de la Tropicana ¡Conchita Alvarez y sus muchachos!

Ad lib. background voices

¡Conchita!

Spoken: Welcome to Havana, how is everyone, don't tell me, I think I know.
(2° see block text)

Your life is go-ing cra-zy and you don't know what to do,— your

busi-ness it went un-der and you're com-ing down with flu. Your son is go-ing stea-dy but his

girl-friend's name is Frank, your daugh-ter's made the eve-ning news by

hold - ing up a bank. But you don't cry - ay - ay,—— in - stead you

fly - ay - ay—— and when you get down here—— all your wor - ries dis - ap - pear—— dear.

Wel - come—— to Ha - va - na where the world is on va - ca - tion,

wel - come—— to Ha - va - na for the par - ty of your life.——

Verse 2:
CONCHITA *(spoken)*
It's the greatest city in the world.
Believe me, I know,
I've been around.
(sung)
Morocco has the Casbah
But it also has the stench,
And Nice is very nice
But then it also has the French.
It's much too cold in Sweden,
It's much too hot in Rome,
And if you go to London
Well you might as well stay home.
But here the air is clean
And here the palms are green,
So come and be my guest
ALL
And let Conchita do the rest.

CONCHITA
Welcome to Havana,
Have a drink, have a double,
Welcome to Havana
Where the moon is full and round.
Back in Indiana
Life is gloom and doom and trouble,
Being in Havana
Makes my heart begin to pound.

THE MERMAID'S TALE

Music by Barry Manilow. Lyrics by Bruce Sussman & Jack Feldman.

MERMAIDS

Long a-go in a sim-pler time when
fell in love with a maid-en fair, a

pi-rates ruled the sea, there lived a brave and right-eous man who fought to keep men free.
girl with eme-rald eyes, then one day pi-rates stole a-shore and took her as their prize.

Ah_____

1.
he fought to keep men free.
the

Ah_____

Ah_____

Ah_____

(2.) He

girl with the eme- rald eyes. They dragged her scream- ing to their ship,

they in- tro- duced her to the whip, they drank and

swore and made her par- ty to their sins, and

there our tale be - gins.

EL BRAVO!

Music by Barry Manilow. Lyrics by Bruce Sussman & Jack Feldman.

103

Verse 2:
Do what you will
Cowards and swine,
Attack and bully me
And crack your whips.
No cry of agony
Will pass my lips
My heart is his,
His strength is mine.

Where is the man I adore?
El Bravo!
¿Donde esta mi amor?
El Bravo!
Friend of the weak
And the poor and the meek,
And the chained and the pained
And the soon-to-be-dead
And the sad and the sick
Darling quick,
It's the nick of time
El Bravo!
El Bravo!
El Bravo!

WHO NEEDS TO DREAM?
(Reprise)

Music by Barry Manilow & Artie Butler. Lyrics by Bruce Sussman & Jack Feldman.

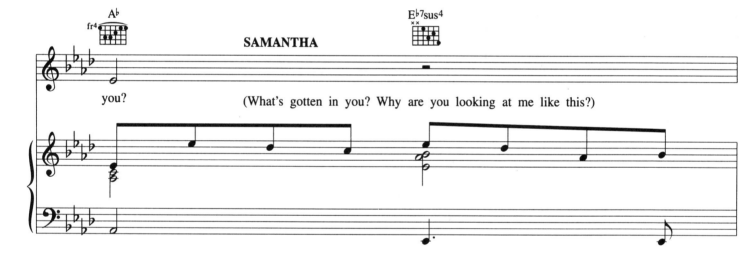

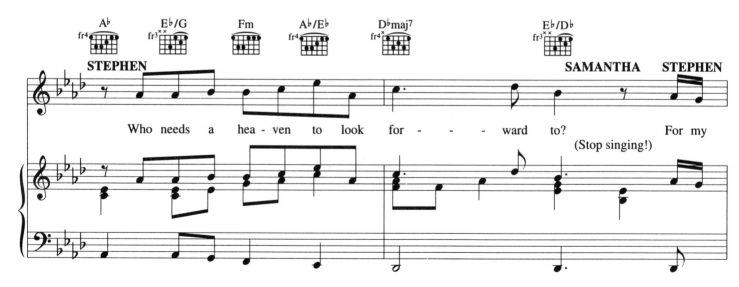

COPACABANA
(At The Copa)

Music by Barry Manilow. Lyrics by Bruce Sussman & Jack Feldman.

109

va - na   at____ the Co - pa   Co - pa - ca - ba - na,____

mu - sic and pas - sion were al - ways the fa - shion at the Co - pa____

STEPHEN   **RICO**

they fell in   he lost her love.

ENSEMBLE

Co - pa,____

Verse 2:

LOLA
His name was Rico,
He wore a diamond.
SAM
He was escorted to his chair,
He saw Lola dancing there.
GLADYS
And when she finished,
He called her over,

CONCHITA
But Rico went a bit too far,
Tony sailed across the bar.
RICO
And then the punches flew
And chairs were smashed in two.
STEPHEN
There was blood and a single gunshot,
But just who shot who?